1. A Song

2. Berceuse

French traditional

da capo al fine

3. Miniature March

Play staccato: the notes well detached.

4. Waltz

5. Scottish Air

Low notes need plenty of air but little breath pressure.

6. Pony Trot

For Henny Oey

First Book of Descant Recorder Solos

---

for descant (soprano) recorder and piano

by

WALTER BERGMANN

© 1980 by Faber Music Ltd
First published in 1980 by Faber Music Ltd
3 Queen Square London WC1N 3AU
Cover design by Shirley Tucker
Printed in England by Caligraving Ltd

ISBN 0-571-50587-2

To buy Faber Music publications or to find out about the full range of titles available
please contact your local music retailer or Faber Music sales enquiries:

Faber Music Ltd, Burnt Mill, Elizabeth Way, Harlow, CM20 2HX England
Tel: +44 (0)1279 82 89 82   Fax: +44 (0)1279 82 89 83
sales@fabermusic.com   www.fabermusic.com

Faber Music Limited

London

Contents

1. A Song ... 1
2. Berceuse *French traditional* ... 1
3. Miniature March ... 1
4. Waltz ... 2
5. Scottish Air ... 2
6. Pony Trot ... 2
7. A la Claire Fontaine *French traditional* ... 3
8. The Passion Chorale *old German* ... 3
9. Austrian Ländler ... 3
10. Old German Christmas Song ... 4
11. La Volta ... 4
12. Folk Tune ... 4
13. Les Bouffons *from Arbeau's* Orchésographie ... 5
14. Gavotte *G. F. Handel* ... 5
15. Almande *Claude Gervaise* ... 6
16. Minuet *Francis Dieupart* ... 6
17. Polka *Czech traditional* ... 7
18. Variations on 'Lavender's Blue' ... 7
19. A Christmas Song *J. S. Bach* ... 8
20. Babiole *J. J. Naudot* ... 8
21. Musette *E. P. Chédeville* ... 8
22. Italian Folk Song ... 9
23. Minuet *J. Paisible* ... 9
24. Andante from Partita No. 1 *G. Ph. Telemann* ... 10
25. Duet ... 10
26. Hornpipe ... 11
27. Norwegian Call ... 11
28. Gavotte *J. C. Pepusch* ... 12
29. Grave *J. Paisible* ... 12
30. Waltz Variations *Benjamin Britten* ... 13
31. Chaconne from 'The Fairy Queen' *Henry Purcell* ... 14
32. Canzonetta *Carl Loewe* ... 15

4. Waltz

5. Scottish Air

Low notes need plenty of air but little breath pressure.

6. Pony Trot

7. A la Claire Fontaine

French traditional

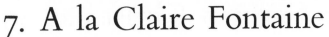

8. The Passion Chorale

Old German

Chorales are the hymns of the German Protestant Church. This 'Passion' Chorale is best known through J. S. Bach's Church compositions, e.g. St. Matthew Passion.

9. Austrian Ländler

4

10. Old German Christmas Song

11. La Volta

Old English

12. Folk Tune

13. Les Bouffons

from Arbeau's *Orchésographie* (1589)

Bouffons = comedians. With the accompaniment, this piece should give the effect of the 'pipe and tabor' (fife and drum).

14. Gavotte

G. F. HANDEL
(1685–1759)

The characteristic of the gavotte as a dance is its gracefulness. Handel wrote six sonatas for recorder with accompaniment and used the recorder in his chamber music and operas. This gavotte is the finale of one of his operas.

15. Almande

CLAUDE GERVAISE
(16th century)

From a collection of Dances published by Pierre Attaignant in Paris in 1557. Tempo: one dance-step to a crotchet.

16. Minuet

FRANCIS DIEUPART
(died 1740)

Francis Dieupart, whose first name is often mistakenly quoted as Charles, came to England in the first years of the 18th century. His harpsichord suites were known and admired by Bach.

17. Polka

Czech traditional

The polka is a Czech dance of moderate speed (♩ = *c.* 88).

18. Variations on 'Lavender's Blue'

19. A Christmas Song: 'O Jesulein süss'

J. S. BACH
(1685–1750)

Tenderly

20. Babiole

J. J. NAUDOT
(18th century)

Allegro

Babiole = bauble. Naudot composed many works for 'musette [a small French bagpipe] or flûte à bec [recorder] or flûte traversière [flute] or oboe etc.' This is one of them. To achieve the rhythm indicated play the first note very slightly longer than its note value and the third note (the crotchet) as a quaver followed by a quaver rest.

21. Musette

E. P. CHÈDEVILLE
(1696–1762)

p legato

fine

da capo al fine

A musette was both a French bagpipe and a dance-like piece of pastoral character. Like Naudot's 'Babiole' (No. 20) this 'Musette' was intended for a variety of musical instruments.

22. Italian Folk Song

Traditional

23. Minuet

J. PAISIBLE
(*c.* 1650–1721)

Paisible was a famous recorder player and a prolific composer for the instrument.

24. Andante from Partita No. 1

G. PH. TELEMANN
(1681–1767)

Play Andante (not Adagio) in **4/4** (not **8/8**).

25. Duet

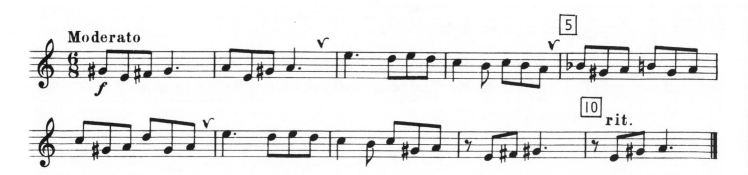

The piano part can be played on a second descant (soprano) recorder.

26. Hornpipe

27. Norwegian Call

Play very slowly to create an atmosphere of complete tranquility.

28. Gavotte

J. C. PEPUSCH
(1667–1752)

Pepusch, a German emigrant to England, wrote sonatas and chamber music for the recorder, and arranged the music for John Gay's *Beggar's Opera* (1728). This 'Gavotte' is taken from one of his sonatas for treble recorder and figured bass.

29. Grave

J. PAISIBLE
(c. 1650–1721)

30. Waltz Variations

BENJAMIN BRITTEN
(1913–1976)

This piece was written by Benjamin Britten for the piano before he was 12, and has been arranged (by permission of the composer) for descant recorder and piano. Britten, who played the recorder himself and was until his death President of the Society of Recorder Players in Great Britain, has used the recorder in several works including *Noyes Fludde, A Midsummer Night's Dream* and the *Alpine Suite* (for recorder trio).

© 1970 by Faber Music Ltd. This arrangement © 1980 by Faber Music Ltd.

31. Chaconne from 'The Fairy Queen'

HENRY PURCELL
(1659–1695)

32. Canzonetta

CARL LOEWE
(1796–1869)

This beautiful melody is composed for the voice and should be played accordingly. It has the greatest effect when played very slowly.

STANDARD FINGERING CHART

Figures indicate covered holes.
A figure with a stroke through it indicates a half-covered hole.

⸺ Thumbhole covered ⸺

c''	c''#/d''♭	d''	d''#/e''♭	e''	f''	f''#/g''♭	g''	g''#/a''♭	a''	a''#/b''♭	b''	c'''
1 2 3	1 2 3	1 2 3	1 2 3	1 2 3	1 2 3	1 2 3	1 2 3	1 2	1 2	1 3	1	2
4 5 6 7	4 5 6 ~~7~~	4 5 6	4 5 ~~6~~	4 5	4 6 7	5 6		4 5 ~~6~~		4		

⸺ Thumbhole open ⸺

	d'''	
1 2	2	2 3
		4 5 6

⸺ Thumbhole partly covered ⸺

e'''	f'''	f'''#/g'''♭	g'''	g'''#/a'''♭	a'''	a'''#/b'''♭	b'''	c''''	c''''#/d''''♭	d''''
1 2 3	1 2 3	1 2 3	1 2 3	1 2	1 2	1 2	1 2	1	1 3	1 3
4 5	4 6	5	4		4 5 6	4 5	4 5	4 5	4 5 7	4 6

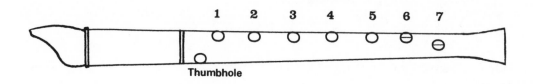

1   2   3   4   5   6   7

Thumbhole

TRILL (SHAKE) FINGERING CHART

Most trills are played with the normal fingerings, but sometimes this is unduly difficult, or even impossible. This chart shows the exceptional fingerings most frequently used. As in the Standard Fingering Chart, figures indicate covered holes, figures with a stroke through them indicating half-covered holes. A sharp or flat between the note and the trill sign (*tr*) concerns the upper note. The letters l (lower note), u (upper note) or b (both) indicate which of the notes require the exceptional fingering.

— Thumbhole covered —

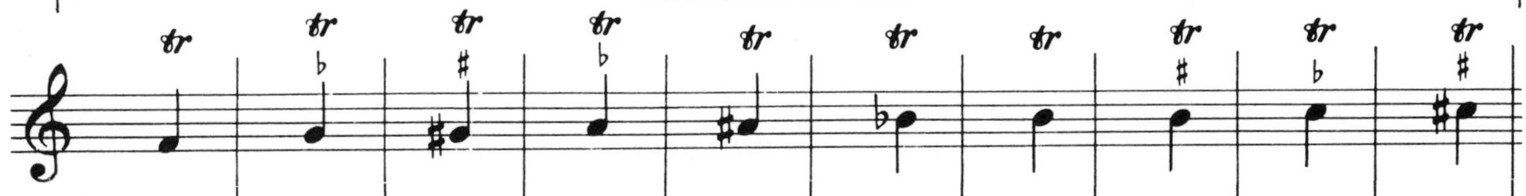

tr	*tr* b	*tr* #	*tr* b	*tr*	*tr*	*tr*	*tr* #	*tr* b	*tr* #
1	1	1	1	1	1tr		1tr		
2	2					2		2tr	2
3		3	3	3tr	3tr				3
4tr	4	4	4	4	4				4
5	5	5tr	5tr						5tr
6	6tr	6tr	~~6~~		6				6
7	7tr	~~7~~			7				
u	**l**	**b**	**b**	**u**	**b**	**l**	**u**	**u**	**l**

— Thumbhole open —

tr b	*tr*	*tr*	*tr* b	*tr*
1	1		1	1
2	2	2	2	2
3	3	3	3	3
4	4	4	4	4
5	5tr	5	5tr	
6	6	6tr	6	6
7tr	7			7tr
b	**b**	**u**	**l**	**b**

— Thumbhole partly covered —

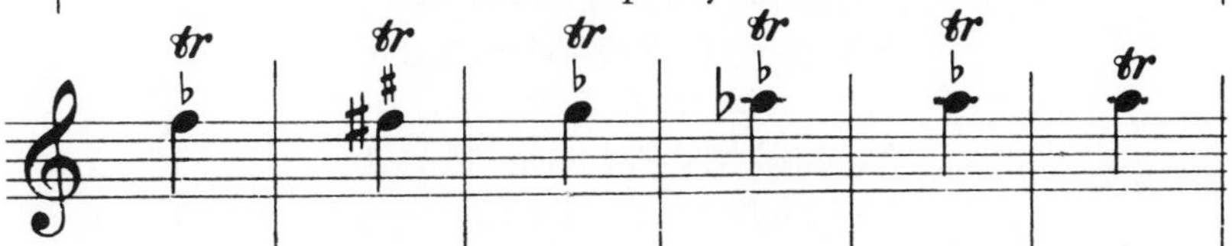

tr b	*tr* # #	*tr* b	*tr* b b	*tr* b	*tr*
1	1	1	1	1	1
2	2	2	2	2	2
3	~~3~~ tr		3tr		~~3~~
	4	4	4	4	4
5			5	5	5
~~6~~ tr		~~6~~ tr	6	6	6tr
			7 #	7tr	7tr
l	**l**	**l**	**l**	**l**	**b**

RECORDER MUSIC
from Faber Music

MALCOLM ARNOLD
Fantasy for Descant Recorder
ISBN 0-571-51049-3

WALTER BERGMANN
First Book of Treble Solos
ISBN 0-571-50546-5

First Book of Descant Solos
ISBN 0-571-50587-2

Second Book of Descant Solos
ISBN 0-571-50676-3

BONSOR, BRIAN
Play Country Dances
ISBN 0-571-51004-3

Really Easy Recorder Book
ISBN 0-571-51037-X

ALAN GOUT
Play Spirituals
ISBN 0-571-51458-8

GEORGE FRIDERIC HANDEL
Complete Recorder Sonatas
ISBN 0-571-50566-X

PAUL HARRIS
Improve your sight-reading! Descant Recorder Grades 1-3
ISBN 0-571-51373-5

MARLENE HOBSBAWM
Me and My Recorder Part 1
ISBN 0-571-51045-0

Me and My Recorder Part 2
ISBN 0-571-51052-3

ANDREW LLOYD WEBBER
Cats Selection (recorder duet and piano)
ISBN 0-571-50905-3

FABER MUSIC · 3 QUEEN SQUARE · LONDON
www.fabermusic.com

ISBN 0-571-50448-5

9 780571 504480 >